INTRODUCTION

C000118305

This booklet by the Astronomy Corresponc
Hendrie, provides a convenient guide to seein
the naked eye. The twelve monthly charts on p   ......ow those objects
above the horizon late in the evening. The charts have been drawn for the latitude of London (51°30' north) but may be used for any part of the British Isles.
Opposite each chart are notes on the visibility of the planets and phases of the
Moon. A summary of recent and forthcoming developments in space appears on
page 29 along with comments on opportunities for seeing the principal meteor
showers during the year. A detailed explanation of the astronomical terms used
and how the various phenomena arise can be found in the fully illustrated *The
Times Night Sky Companion.*

The Changing Aspect of the Night Sky

From our position on the surface of the Earth, the stars appear to lie on the
inside of a spherical surface, called the celestial sphere. Because the stars are so
far away their directions remain essentially unchanged when seen from different
parts of the Earth's orbit. The diagram on the inside cover (*see* left) shows one
such direction, indicated by the arrow pointing to the First Point of Aries. The
stars that lie behind the Sun as seen from the Earth at the beginning of April
each year will, by October, be in the opposite part of the sky to the Sun and be
due south at midnight. The arrow points to Pisces (where the First point of Aries
now lies) and looking at the October chart Pisces is indeed in the southern sky
but it does not appear at all on the April chart, being behind the Sun and in the
daytime sky. More generally, a line from the Sun through the position of the
Earth points towards the stars seen near the lower centre of the chart for that
month. Remembering this, one can relate the positions of the other planets in
their orbits to where they will be in the sky, though they will not always be on
the monthly chart, being too near to the Sun in direction.

Time of Observation and Location

Greenwich Mean Time (GMT but also known as Universal Time) is used
throughout this booklet. When in force, British Summer Time (BST) is 1 hour
ahead of GMT, e.g. 23h BST is 22h GMT. Strictly speaking, the charts are only
correct in the stars they show above the horizon for an observer near London
(Greenwich). As one moves north fewer stars appear above the southern horizon. Movement east or west along the same latitude does not alter what stars
can be seen, but only when they can be seen.

Using the Charts

The charts show the brighter stars above the horizon for London at 23h (11pm)
at the beginning, 22h (10pm) in the middle and 21h (9pm) at the end of each
month. The stars rise four minutes earlier each night or two hours earlier each

month, being back in their same positions at the same time after a year. Thus, for instance, the aspect of the heavens at 23h on 1 April is the same as on 1 May at 21h or 1 March at 01h. By remembering this rule, the chart applicable to any hour throughout the year may be found. This rule does not apply to the Moon and planets. The charts show the whole sky visible at one time with the zenith, the point directly overhead, at the centre of the chart. Note that the Pole Star (Polaris) occupies the same position on every chart being close to one of the two points around which the whole star sphere appears to revolve. It is easily found in relation to Ursa Major at all times of the year and is useful in defining due north. Ursa Major's seven brightest stars form the Plough. The end two stars (the Pointers) are always in line with Polaris. If the observer faces south with the Pole Star to his back and the appropriate chart held up as one would read the booklet, the constellations depicted above the southern horizon should be to the front, with the eastern aspect to the left and western horizon to the right.

Explanatory Notes on Terms Used

The Moon – the phase and position are given for about 22h on every other day when it is above the horizon at that time. The average time between like phases (e.g. full to full) is 29.5 days, 2 days longer than it takes to return amongst the same stars. It moves eastwards by its own diameter every hour.

The Planets – are shown in the position they occupy about the middle of the month unless otherwise indicated, and for Venus and Mars an arrow shows by its length the movement during the month. Planets crossing the meridian (i.e. due south) before midnight are said to be evening stars while those crossing the meridian after midnight are morning stars. A planet is in opposition to the Sun when it is in the opposite part of the sky to the Sun and therefore due south at midnight. (Mercury and Venus can never be at opposition.) It is then at its closest and brightest for that year. For a few weeks on either side of opposition, motion among the stars, instead of being from west to east as usual, is from east to west and is called retrograde. At the turning points, where motion is reversed, the planet is said to be stationary. A planet coming in line with the Earth and the Sun is said to be in superior conjunction with the Sun if it lies beyond the Sun but at inferior conjunction if it lies between the Earth and the Sun. Only Mercury and Venus can be at inferior conjunction. Planets can also be in conjunction with others when close in the sky. Mercury and Venus are said to be at greatest elongation when at their greatest apparent distance from the Sun, either east (evening) or west (morning). They can never be high in the sky late at night. Mercury is not observable in a dark sky from the British Isles and may require binoculars. It is always too near the sun to be included on the monthly charts. Uranus is visible at times to the naked eye but will probably require binoculars for identification. Neptune always requires optical aid. Pluto requires a moderate-sized telescope and is not mentioned in the monthly notes. Opposition in 2000 is on 1 June, the 14th magnitude planet being in Ophiuchus.

ECLIPSES IN 2000

21 JANUARY

This total eclipse of the Moon will be visible from N. Russia, Europe including the British Isles, N.W. Africa, the Atlantic Ocean, the Arctic and the Americas. The Moon enters the penumbra at 2h 03m, the umbra at 3h 01m and totality begins at 4h 05m. The middle of the eclipse is at 4h 44m, totality ends at 5h 22m, and the Moon leaves the umbra at 6h 25m.

5 FEBRUARY

This partial eclipse of the Sun will be visible from parts of the Indian Ocean and Antarctica.

1 JULY

This partial eclipse of the Sun will be visible from the southeastern Pacific Ocean and the southern parts of the South American peninsular.

16 JULY

This total eclipse of the Moon will be visible from Australasia, Antarctica, much of the Pacific Ocean, Japan, China, S.E. Asia, India and eastern Siberia. The middle of the eclipse is about 14h.

31 JULY

This partial eclipse of the Sun will be visible from north and west Russia, northern Scandinavia, Greenland, the Arctic Ocean and N.W. North America.

25 DECEMBER

This partial eclipse of the Sun will be visible from Mexico, the Caribbean, much of North America, the western Atlantic Ocean and southern Greenland.

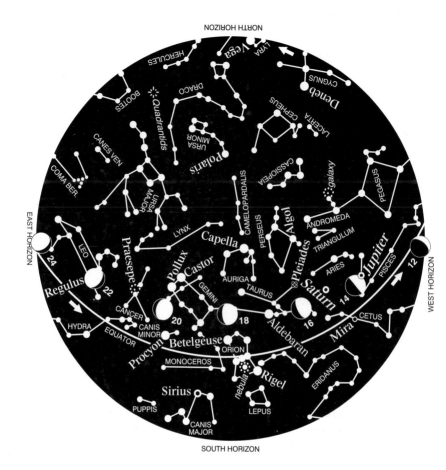

JANUARY 1, 23h (11 pm)

The aspect of the sky (apart from the Moon and Planets) will be approximately the same in other months at the following times:

October 1, 05h: November 1, 03h: December 1, 01h: February 1, 21h: March 1, 19h.

The time in these notes is that of the Greenwich meridian.

4

JANUARY

The Planets

MERCURY begins the year as a morning object. After superior conjunction on the 16th it becomes an evening star remaining too near the Sun for observation.

VENUS is a brilliant -4.0 magnitude in the SE sky before dawn, rising 3 hours before the Sun on the 1st but only 1.5 hours before sunrise by the 31st. Moon to the north on the 3rd.

MARS is 1.0 magnitude and in Aquarius. Its rapid eastwards motion against the stars will keep it in the western evening sky until June, setting between 20h and 21h. Moon to the south on the 10th.

JUPITER is a bright -2.1 magnitude in Pisces setting about 0h by the 31st. Moon nearby on the 14th.

SATURN is in Aries, 0.2 magnitude, setting at 01h by end month. Stationary on the 13th. Moon nearby on the 15th.

URANUS is in Capricornus throughout the year. The 5.7 magnitude planet requires binoculars or a telescope and a chart showing fainter stars for identification.

NEPTUNE also remains in Capricornus throughout 2000 and at 8th magnitude requires similar aids to Uranus for positive identification. In conjunction with the Sun on the 24th.

The Moon

New Moon 6d 18h
First quarter 14d 14h
Full Moon 21d 05h
Last quarter 28d 08h

Eclipse on the 21st: *see* page 3.
The Earth: at perihelion 3d 05h (147 million km)

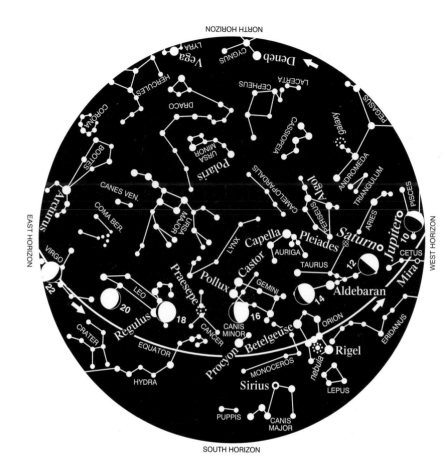

FEBRUARY 1, 23h (11 pm)

The aspect of the sky (apart from the Moon and Planets) will be approximately the same in other months at the following times:

November 1, 05h: December 1, 03h: January 1, 01h: March 1, 21h: April 1, 19h.

The time in these notes is that of the Greenwich meridian.

FEBRUARY

The Planets

MERCURY is an evening star, setting nearly 2 hours after the Sun by greatest eastern elongation on the 15th (18 degrees). Until mid-month the -0.5 magnitude planet will be observable in twilight low in the southwestern sky. Thin crescent Moon nearby on the 6th.

VENUS rises about 06h during February but as the Sun will rise earlier each day, it will fade into the brightening dawn sky. Venus will then be too near the Sun to be seen in a dark sky until November. Moon to the north on the 2nd.

MARS moves eastwards from Aquarius into Pisces in early February and then into Cetus, being 1.2 magnitude in mid-month. Moon to the south on the 8th.

JUPITER moves from Pisces into Aries in mid-February, the -2.2 magnitude planet setting about 22h 30m by the 29th. Moon nearby on the 10th.

SATURN is in Aries setting soon after 23h by end month. Moon nearby on the 11th.

URANUS is in conjunction with the Sun on the 6th and is not observable.

NEPTUNE rises an hour before the Sun by the 29th.

The Moon

New Moon 5d 13h
First quarter 12d 23h
Full Moon 19d 16h
Last quarter 27d 04h

Moon near Aldebaran on the 13th.
Eclipse on the 5th: *see* page 3.

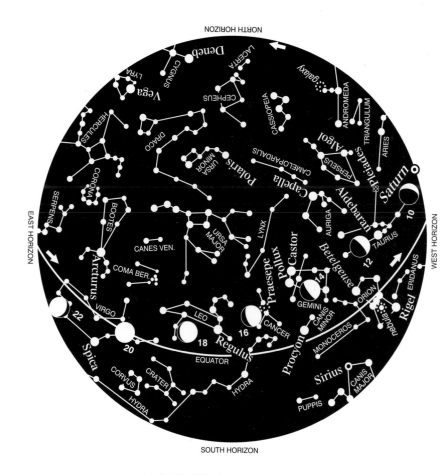

MARCH 1, 23h (11 pm)

The aspect of the sky (apart from the Moon and Planets) will be approximately the same in other months at the following times:

December 1, 05h: January 1, 03h: February 1, 01h: April 1, 21h.

The time in these notes is that of the Greenwich meridian.

MARCH

The Planets

MERCURY passes through inferior conjunction on the 1st to become a morning star. At greatest western elongation (28 degrees) on the 28th, it remains too near the Sun this month to be observable.

VENUS is a morning star but is too near the Sun for observation.

MARS moves from Cetus into Aries in March, fading slowly to 1.4 magnitude and setting about 21h by the 31st. Moon to the south on the 8th.

JUPITER is -2.1 magnitude and in Aries setting by 21h in late March. Moon to the south on the 9th.

SATURN is also in Aries and 0.3 magnitude and sets at 21h 30m by the 31st. Moon nearby on the 9th–10th.

URANUS rises about 04h by end March. Moon to the south on the 31st.

NEPTUNE rises about 03h 30m by the 31st. Moon to the south on the 30th.

The Moon

New Moon 6d 05h
First quarter 13d 07h
Full Moon 20d 05h
Last quarter 28d 00h

The Earth: Spring Equinox 20d 08h.

APRIL 1, 23h (11 pm)

The aspect of the sky (apart from the Moon and Planets) will be approximately the same in other months at the following times:

December 1, 07h: January 1, 05h: February 1, 03h: March 1, 01h: May 1, 21h.

The time in these notes is that of the Greenwich meridian.

APRIL

The Planets

MERCURY is a morning star throughout April but is too near the Sun for observation.

VENUS is also a morning star but like Mercury is too near the Sun to be seen.

MARS is 1.5 magnitude and moves from Aries into Taurus in late April, setting about 21h. Moon nearby on the 6th. Mars north of Jupiter on the 6th and Saturn on the 16th.

JUPITER is in Aries, setting only minutes after the Sun by the 30th. Moon to the south on the 6th.

SATURN is in Aries but sets soon after the Sun by end April. Moon to the south on the 6th.

URANUS is in Capricornus rising by 02h 30m by the 30th. Moon nearby on the 28th.

NEPTUNE is also in Capricornus and rises before 02h by end April. Moon nearby on the 27th.

The Moon

New Moon 4d 18h
First quarter 11d 14h
Full Moon 18d 18h
Last quarter 26d 19h

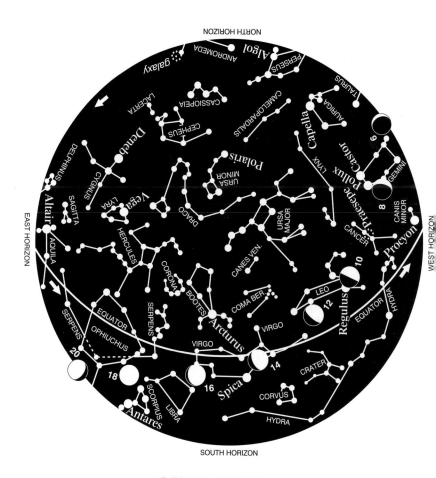

MAY 1, 23h (11 pm)

The aspect of the sky (apart from the Moon and Planets) will be approximately the same in other months at the following times:

January 1, 07h: February 1, 05h: March 1, 03h: April 1, 01h: June 1, 21h.

The time in these notes is that of the Greenwich meridian.

MAY

The Planets

MERCURY is at superior conjunction on the 9th and then becomes an evening object, setting 2 hours after the Sun by the 31st when it will still be 0 magnitude. It should be visible in northwestern twilight during the last week of May. Mars to the south on the 19th.

VENUS rises only minutes before the Sun and will not be observable in May.

MARS is in Taurus and may be glimpsed early in the month in the northwest twilight. By the 31st it sets less than an hour after the Sun. Moon to the south on the 5th.

JUPITER is in conjunction with the Sun on the 8th and then becomes a morning star but too near the Sun to be seen.

SATURN is at conjunction on the 10th, moving into the morning sky but too near the Sun for observation.

URANUS is in Capricornus and rises soon after midnight by the 31st. Stationary on the 25th. Moon to the south on the 25th.

NEPTUNE rises about 23h 30m by end May. Stationary on the 8th. Moon to the south on the 24th.

The Moon

New Moon 4d 04h
First quarter 10d 20h
Full Moon 18h 08h
Last quarter 26d 12h

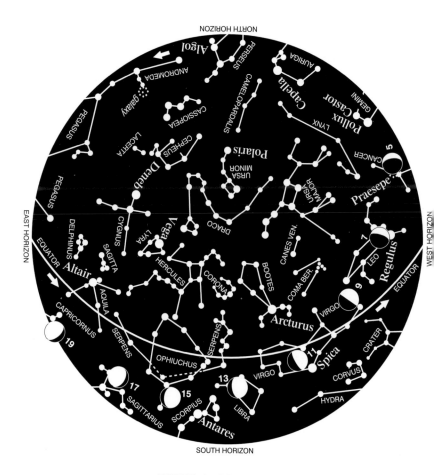

JUNE 1, 23h (11 pm)

The aspect of the sky (apart from the Moon and Planets)
will be approximately the same in other months at the
following times:

**February 1, 07h: March 1, 05h: April 1, 03h:
May 1, 01h: July 1, 21h.**

The time in these notes is that of the Greenwich meridian.

14

JUNE

The Planets

MERCURY is 0 magnitude on the 1st, setting 2 hours after the Sun, reaching greatest eastern elongation (24 degrees) on the 9th. Mercury should be visible low in the northwest after sunset during the first week of June. Moon nearby on the 3rd.

VENUS is at superior conjunction on the 11th and will not be observable this month.

MARS is in Taurus but sets less than an hour after the Sun and will not be observable in June.

JUPITER is in Taurus and -2.0 magnitude. By the 30th it will rise about 01h 30m. Moon to the south on the 1st and 29th.

SATURN is also in Taurus rising about the same time as Jupiter. Moon to the south on the 1st and 29th.

URANUS rises soon after 22h by the 30th. Moon to the south on the 21st.

NEPTUNE rises about 21h 30m at end month. Moon to the south on the 20th.

The Moon

New Moon 2d 12h
First quarter 9d 03h
Full Moon 16d 22h
Last quarter 25d 01h

The Earth: Summer Solstice on 21d 02h.

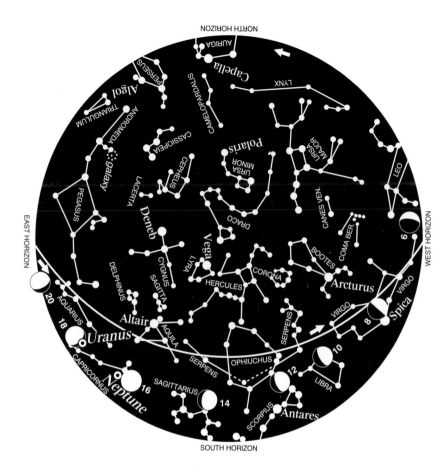

JULY 1, 23h (11 pm)

The aspect of the sky (apart from the Moon and Planets)
will be approximately the same in other months at the
following times:

**April 1, 05h: May 1, 03h: June 1, 01h:
August 1, 21h: September 1, 19h.**

The time in these notes is that of the Greenwich meridian.

16

JULY

The Planets

MERCURY is at inferior conjunction on the 6th and is then a morning star at greatest western elongation (20 degrees) on the 27th. Rising 1.5 hours before the Sun, the 0 magnitude planet should be visible low in northeastern twilight.

VENUS is an evening star, setting less than an hour after the Sun, and is unlikely to be seen.

MARS is in conjunction with the Sun on the 1st and will not be observable this month.

JUPITER is -2.1 magnitude and in Taurus, rising before midnight (0h) by the 31st. Moon nearby on the 26th.

SATURN is 0.2 magnitude and in Taurus rising before 0h by end July. Moon to the south on the 26th.

URANUS is in Capricornus rising about sunset on the 31st. Moon nearby on the 18th.

NEPTUNE is at opposition on the 27th. Moon nearby on the 16th–17th.

The Moon

New Moon 1d 19h
First quarter 8d 13h
Full Moon 16d 14h
Last quarter 24d 11h
New Moon 31d 02h

Eclipses on the 1st, 16th and 31st: *see* page 3.
The Earth: at aphelion 4d 00h (152 million km).

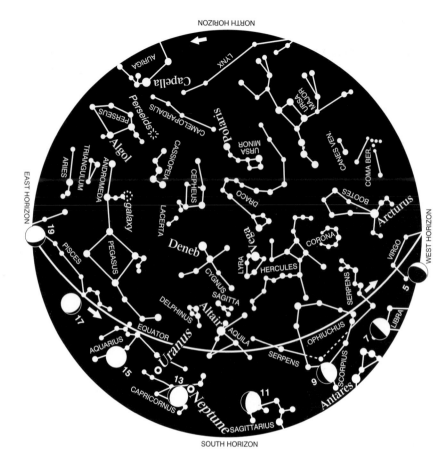

AUGUST 1, 23h (11 pm)

The aspect of the sky (apart from the Moon and Planets)
will be approximately the same in other months at the
following times:

June 1, 03h: July 1, 01h: September 1, 21h:
October 1, 19h: November 1, 17h.

The time in these notes is that of the Greenwich meridian.

18

AUGUST

The Planets

MERCURY at -1 magnitude should be visible in morning twilight until mid-month. Very close to Mars on the 10th. At superior conjunction on the 22nd, it then becomes an evening star too near the Sun for observation.

VENUS sets too soon after the Sun for easy observation until October.

MARS is 1.8 magnitude and in Cancer, moving on into Leo in late August, rising by 03h 30m by the 31st. Moon very close on the 28th.

JUPITER is -2.3 and in Taurus, rising about 22h by the 31st. Moon to the south on the 23rd.

SATURN is 0.2 magnitude and also in Taurus, rising about 21h 30m by end August. Moon to the south on the 22nd.

URANUS is 5.7 magnitude and like Neptune needs optical aid for identification. At opposition on the 11th, it sets about 03h by the 31st. Moon nearby on the 14th.

NEPTUNE is 7.9 magnitude, rising about 02h end month. Moon nearby on the 13th.

The Moon

First quarter 7d 01h
Full Moon 15d 05h
Last quarter 22d 19h
New Moon 29d 10h

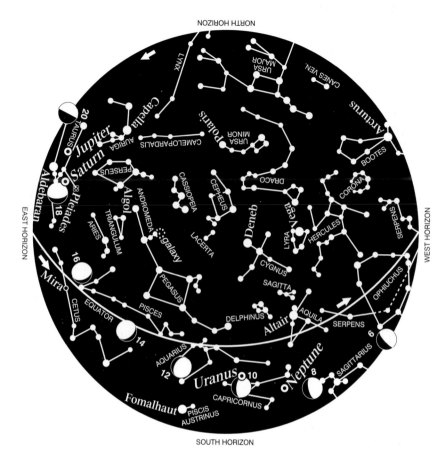

SEPTEMBER 1, 23h (11 pm)

The aspect of the sky (apart from the Moon and Planets) will be approximately the same in other months at the following times:

July 1, 03h: August 1, 01h: October 1, 21h: November 1, 19h: December 1, 17h.

The time in these notes is that of the Greenwich meridian.

SEPTEMBER

The Planets

MERCURY is in the evening sky but too close to the Sun for observation.

VENUS is also an evening star, low in the west and in a very bright sky this month.

MARS is 1.8 magnitude in Leo and rises soon after 03h throughout the month. Closest to Regulus on the 16th. Moon nearby on the 25th.

JUPITER is -2.5 magnitude and in Taurus, rising about 20h by the 30th. Stationary on the 29th. Moon to the south on the 19th.

SATURN is 0 magnitude and in Taurus, rising before 20h by end September. Stationary on the 12th. Moon to the south on the 18th.

URANUS is in Capricornus setting soon after 01h by the 30th. Moon to the south on the 10th.

NEPTUNE is also in Capricornus rising about 0h by end month. Moon to the south on the 9th.

The Moon

First quarter 5d 16h
Full Moon 13d 20h
Last quarter 21d 01h
New Moon 27d 20h

The Earth: Autumn Equinox on 22d 17h.

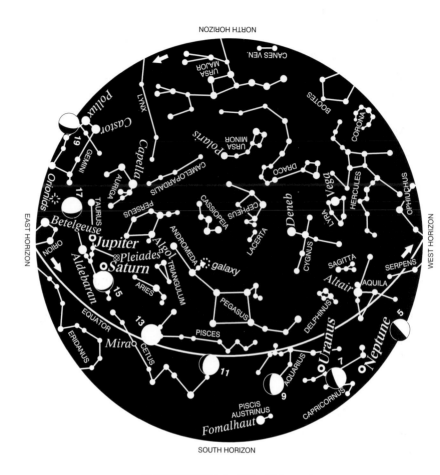

OCTOBER 1, 23h (11 pm)

The aspect of the sky (apart from the Moon and Planets) will be approximately the same in other months at the following times:

August 1, 03h: September 1, 01h: November 1, 21h:
December 1, 19h: January 1, 17h.

The time in these notes is that of the Greenwich meridian.

OCTOBER

The Planets

MERCURY is at greatest eastern elongation (26 degrees) on the 6th but is too near the Sun for observation. At inferior conjunction on the 30th, it then becomes a morning star.

VENUS is -4.0 magnitude and in the evening sky and should become more easily visible by the 31st when it sets more than an hour after the Sun. Antares 3 degrees south on the 26th. Moon nearby on the 30th.

MARS passes from Leo into Virgo later in the month, rising about 03h throughout October. Moon to the north on the 24th.

JUPITER is a bright -2.7 magnitude, rising at 18h by the 31st. Moon nearby on the 16th–17th.

SATURN is -0.2 magnitude and rises soon after sunset by end October. Moon nearby on the 15th–16th.

URANUS sets about 23h by the 31st. Stationary on the 26th. Moon nearby on the 7th–8th.

NEPTUNE sets about 22h by end October. Stationary on the 15th. Moon nearby on the 6th.

The Moon

First quarter 5d 11h
Full Moon 13d 09h
Last quarter 20d 08h
New Moon 27d 08h

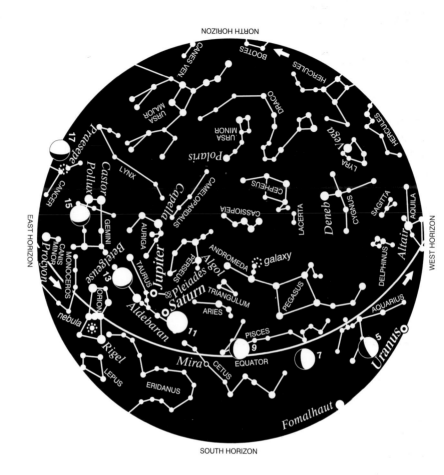

NOVEMBER 1, 23h (11 pm)

The aspect of the sky (apart from the Moon and Planets)
will be approximately the same in other months at the
following times:

September 1, 03h: October 1, 01h: December 1, 21h:
January 1, 19h: February 1, 17h.

The time in these notes is that of the Greenwich meridian.

NOVEMBER

The Planets

MERCURY is at greatest western elongation (19 degrees) on the 15th. Rising 2h before the Sun in mid-month, the -0.5 magnitude morning star should be visible in the southeast during the second half of November. Moon to the north on the 24th.

VENUS is a brilliant -4.1 magnitude evening star, now pulling away from the Sun to rise 3 hours after sunset by the 30th. Moon to the north on the 29th.

MARS is 1.7 magnitude and in Virgo, rising before 03h by the 30th. Moon to the north on the 22nd.

JUPITER is at opposition on the 28th, setting soon after sunrise by the 30th. Moon nearby on the 12th.

SATURN is at opposition on the 19th, setting an hour before Jupiter this month. Both planets are in Taurus. Moon nearby on the 11th.

URANUS sets about 21h by the 30th. Moon to the south on the 4th.

NEPTUNE sets by 20h in late November. Moon to the south on the 3rd and 30th.

The Moon

First quarter 4d 07h
Full Moon 11d 21h
Last quarter 18d 15h
New Moon 25d 23h

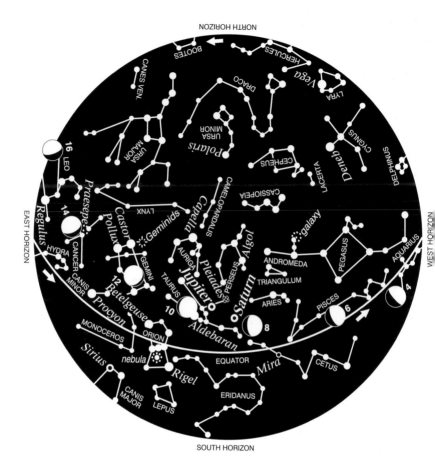

DECEMBER 1, 23h (11 pm)

The aspect of the sky (apart from the Moon and Planets) will be approximately the same in other months at the following times:

September 1, 05h: October 1, 03h: November 1, 01h: January 1, 21h: February 1, 19h.

The time in these notes is that of the Greenwich meridian.

DECEMBER

The Planets

MERCURY is a morning star, closing with the Sun reaching superior conjunction on the 25th, becoming an evening object in the New Year.

VENUS is a brilliant -4.3 magnitude, not setting until 20h by end year. Moon close by on the 29th.

MARS is 1.6 magnitude and in Virgo, rising by 2h 30m by the 31st. North of Spica on the 11th. Moon to the north on the 20th.

JUPITER is in Taurus and -2.7 magnitude, setting about 05h by end December. Moon nearby on the 9th–10th.

SATURN is also in Taurus and 0 magnitude, setting by 04h 30m by the 31st. Moon nearby on the 8th–9th.

URANUS ends the year in Capricornus, setting after 19h by the 31st. Moon nearby on the 1st and 29th.

NEPTUNE is also in Capricornus, setting by 18h 30m at end December. Moon nearby on the 28th.

The Moon

First quarter 4d 04h
Full Moon 11d 09h
Last quarter 18d 01h
New Moon 25d 17h

Eclipse on the 25th : *see* page 3.
The Earth: Winter Solstice on 21d 14h.

THE STARS

The stars are subdivided into magnitudes according to apparent brightness; the lower the number the brighter the star and the larger the dots on our monthly maps. Any star is about 2½ times as bright as one of the next magnitude. The faintest star ordinarily visible to the naked eye is of the 6th magnitude, or just one-hundredth of the brightness of one of the 1st, but that is possible only under a very clear sky. On a moonless night the total number of stars so visible is about 1,000. The faintest object detected with ground-based telescopes is of the 28th magnitude though the Hubble Space Telescope has now reached 30th magnitude.

Zero magnitude (0.0) represents a brightness 2½ times that of a standard first-magnitude star. Brightnesses in excess of this are indicated by a minus sign, the magnitude of Sirius, for example, being -1.47. Venus at its brightest is -4.6 or 145 times as bright as a first-magnitude star. The magnitude of the Full Moon is -12.5, equal to 250,000 first-magnitude stars. The stellar magnitude of the Sun is -26.6 or some 444,000 Full Moons.

The colours of the stars are indications of their surface temperatures. The temperature of a reddish star like Antares is about 3,000 degrees centigrade, and that of a bluish-white star, such as Vega, is about 11,000 degrees. The temperatures of orange, yellow and white stars are intermediate between these extremes.

An examination of the sky on a clear dark night shows that the distribution of stars is far from uniform. While there are distinct clusters of stars, such as the Pleiades and Praesepe, many other groupings consist of stars that just happen to lie in the same direction but at very different distances. The most noticeable concentration of stars is towards what we call the Milky Way, the faint band of light that passes through the following constellations: Puppis, Monoceros, Gemini, Auriga, Perseus, Cassiopeia, Cepheus, Cygnus, Aquila and Sagittarius. Not all of these constellations are above the horizon at any one time. The band of the Milky Way actually extends right round the sky passing through some southern constellations that never rise above the horizon in the British Isles.

Even binoculars show that the Milky Way is made up of thousands of stars, too faint to be seen with the naked eye. Our Sun is situated well away from the centre of a huge, flattened disc-like system of stars 100,000 light years across called the Galaxy. It contains more than 100,000 million stars. When we look along the plane of the disc we see the star-clouds of the Milky Way; but when we look out above or below the plane we see far fewer stars.

From a distance, the Galaxy would look like that in Andromeda, visible to the naked eye only as a hazy oval patch of light. This is one of the nearer galaxies, only two-million light years away. Others have been found in their millions; some may be farther than 10,000 million light years distant, each containing thousands of millions of stars. The central bulge of our Galaxy lies towards the great star clouds in Sagittarius, not easily seen from our latitudes.

THE YEAR IN SPACE 1999–2000

Meteor showers

Some meteors or 'shooting stars' can be seen on any clear, moonless night but at certain times of the year they are much more numerous. When the Earth passes through the stream of debris left in space by a comet orbiting the Sun, a strong shower may be seen as the small particles burn up in the Earth's atmosphere. As the Earth reaches the same part of its orbit about the same date each year, the times of these meteor showers can be predicted, though the number of meteors to be seen in any year is much more difficult to predict. Bright moonlight hides the fainter meteors. In 2000 the Moon will interfere with most of the major showers.

The Quadrantids (2–4 January) appear to come from between Boötes and Draco (see monthly charts for radiant areas), which in early January lies near the northern horizon. The rate has been as high as 100 per hour in some years but is is usually much lower. The Moon will be new on 6th, so conditions are good this year. The Lyrids (21–22 April) come from near Vega but with the Moon full on the 18th conditions could be better. However, the Lyrids are often bright so some may be seen despite the Moon. The Perseids (11–14 August) are an old reliable shower giving 60 or more per hour nearly every year on or about the 12th. With the Moon full on the 15th conditions this year are unfavourable. The radiant of the Orionids (20–22 October) does not rise to a reasonable altitude until after midnight when the last quarter Moon will be rising too, making conditions only fair. The Taurids radiate from the general area below the Pleiades and are spread over several weeks (late October to end November) with rates never high, but there are usually some slow bright meteors.

The Leonids (16–18 November) are normally a weak shower but every 33 years activity increases for a few years when the parent comet Tempel Tuttle is near the Sun: it passed perihelion in February 1998. The rates have been rising over the past few years. On the morning of the 17th November 1998 Western Europe was treated to an exceptional display of bright fireballs. By the 18th when many predicted peak activity, the best was already over with much lower hourly rates and fainter meteors. In 2000 the Moon will be at last quarter on the 18th and near the Leonid radiant, which is in the Sickle of Leo (see December chart). Moonlight will seriously interfere with the number of meteors seen but any bright fireballs could still be spectacular.

The Geminids (12–14 December) like the Perseids is a reliable shower and often the best of the year when the weather is favourable. However, this year the Moon is full on the 11th and near the radiant area and this will severely curtail the numbers seen, usually 60 or more per hour before dawn in a dark sky.

As no one knows for certain exactly when a meteor shower will peak, it is advisable to look on any clear night before and after the predicted dates of maximum activity. Those of us who did this in November 1998 were well rewarded by a once in a lifetime fireball display.

Astronomy

After 323 years the Royal Greenwich Observatory (RGO) was closed down on 31 October 1998. The management of the UK telescopes, mostly sited in the Canary Islands, was transferred to the Royal Observatory Edinburgh and the Nautical Almanac Office to the Rutherford Appleton Laboratory. The RGO was moved to a purpose built building in the grounds of The Observatories in Madingley Road, Cambridge in 1990. The RGO was founded by Charles II in 1675 to obtain more accurate positions of the stars and planets for navigational purposes at sea. The old RGO in Greenwich with buildings designed by Sir Christopher Wren is retained for educational purposes only. Until 1971 the RGO was the responsibility of the Admiralty and the Director of the RGO was also Astronomer Royal, the first being John Flamsteed (1675–1719).

When the Science Research Council took responsibility for the RGO in 1971 they appointed E. Margaret Burbidge as Director but the Government made a separate appointment of Sir Martin Ryle to be Astronomer Royal. Thus Sir Richard Woolley (1956–71) was the last of the line of 11 Directors also to be Astronomer Royal. The dissolution of the Royal Greenwich Observatory, one of the world's oldest astronomical institutions, at a time when space exploration, astronomy and technology are of increasing interest and importance is hard to understand. The savings projected from the closure of the RGO in Cambridge (a very few million pounds per year) are minimal compared with the cost of the Dome being built near the site of the original RGO at Greenwich. It seems that Charles II had a clearer idea of the purpose of his new institution at Greenwich than we have of ours today.

Gamma ray bursts are recorded quite often by orbiting satellites but on 23rd January 1999 the new ROTSE 1 camera array in New Mexico recorded a burst optically less than a minute after the gamma rays were first detected by satellites. The object brightened to 9th magnitude briefly but 10 minutes later it was only one hundredth as bright. Four hours later it was down to 18th magnitude. The reason for these very energetic bursts is uncertain but the distance of this source was put at 9 billion light years from red shift observations made the next night with the 10 meter Keck II telescope in Hawaii. The energy released could be 1000 times greater than that of a supernova explosion, but expended in minutes rather than days. Had any one been looking in the right place for those few seconds, this object, believed to be far out towards the edge of the observable Universe, would have been visible in ordinary binoculars!

The Hubble Space Telescope has been used to take a series of electronic exposures over a 10 day period. When combined into a single image more than 2,500 galaxies were shown, some as faint as 30th magnitude. The estimated distance of the faintest is 12 billion light years. On current 'Big bang' theories, such galaxies would be seen as they were only a few billion years after the creation of the Universe as we know it.

The Year in Space

The solar space observatory (SOHO) was recovered after faulty instructions caused it to lose orientation, the instruments pointing away from the Sun and the communication aerials away from the Earth. Painstaking analysis of possible remedies eventually enabled contact to be re-established, instruments to be brought back to working temperature and observations of the Sun to begin again. However the failure of the last gyroscopes has once again put its long term future in doubt. The observatory is situated about 1.5 million km from the Earth towards the Sun where it is in a semi-stable position, orbiting the Sun with the Earth and allowing continuous observation of the Sun. It has been sending back to Earth outstanding images of the solar atmosphere and giving the Earth some warning of major bursts of solar particles and radiation. Apart from interfering with communications on the Earth and long distance power transmission, solar events can damage the electronics in spacecraft and endanger the lives of astronauts. With greater reliance on electronics and permanently occupied space stations, a better understanding of solar activity is of more than just academic interest.

The future of the Russian Mir Space Station is still undecided. Shortage of money led to plans to de-orbit it in June 1999 but Russia would like a 2 year extension. Now that the first modules of the International Space Station (ISS) are in orbit, the US would like to concentrate on pushing this project ahead. The Russians would like to continue their work on Mir until permanent crews can take over similar research on the ISS, and they would like some equipment to be moved from Mir to the ISS which will not be possible if Mir has been brought down to burn up in the Earth's atmosphere. It is estimated that completion of the ISS will require 36 Shuttle flights over 5 years. Long term occupation will not begin before spring 2000 and will use the earlier modules while the others are being added and readied for use.

The planet Mars is never out of the news for long. There has been the controversy over whether the meteorite found in the Antarctic and generally agreed to have come from Mars, contained the remains of primitive life. The evidence now seems to lean towards the microscopic structures being of the non-living variety. We have seen the excellent pictures of the Mars roving vehicle Sojourner on the Martian surface, moving from rock to rock under control from the Earth, and ever more detailed pictures of the Martian surface from orbiting spacecraft.

The surface of Mars is now known to be far from uniform in nature and has polar caps with water ice or snow and dry ice, ancient volcanoes, deep river valleys, sand dunes, impact craters and many other features parallelling those found on the Earth. The Valles Marineris is the largest feature, a system of canyons that would stretch across the United States from coast to coast. There is now no doubt that at one time, probably more than a billion years ago, Mars had much surface water, perhaps deep oceans and that many features were carved out by running water as on Earth. The volcanoes have probably been dormant for as long. The largest Olympus Mons is three times the height of Mount Everest and nearly as wide across the base as from London to Edinburgh. However the slope of the flanks is very slight and not at all like Mount Fuji for example. The lack of meteorite impact craters in some areas is evidence of extensive lava flows and there are extensive areas of dunes in the polar areas. Clouds and dust storms can obscure the surface and have long been studied from the Earth.

Following on from the successful Mars Pathfinder and Global Surveyor of 1996 two NASA probes should reach Mars in 1999. Mars Climate Orbiter will also study water distribution and take very high resolution pictures of the surface while Mars Polar Lander will land near the south pole to search for water ice. The Japanese Nozomi will now arrive in 2003.

The Mars Surveyor Orbiter & Lander (2001) and a sample return mission (2005) have been cancelled but a new program has been agreed with the intention of returning soil samples to Earth by 2008. A new Mars roving vehicle will collect samples and cache them while a Mars Ascent Vehicle will lift them into orbit to be collected later by a new spacecraft which France will build and which will bring the samples back to Earth from Martian orbit. Ariane 5 may be used for this mission, lifting off in 2005. It will probably carry a lander as well as smaller probes to Mars. Present planning suggests that enough preparation could have been done for a manned mission by 2014. It would of course need the political will to fund such an expensive project, but with the International Space Station to be completed by 2005 the time might be ripe for another grand international space project.